Contents, continued

Name Date Period

Chapter 1
Workbook Activity
1

Emergency Phone List

A. Directions Make a list of emergency phone numbers by filling in the blanks below. Add the names of some people you would call in an emergency. Include a couple of friends and the work phone numbers of family members.

Who to Call	Phone Number
Police Department	________________
Fire Department	________________
Doctor	________________
Poison Control Center	________________
Dentist	________________
Veterinarian	________________
________________	________________
________________	________________
________________	________________
________________	________________

B. Directions Take this list home and put it near your phone. Or copy the list on an index card and keep the card near your phone.

Name Date Period

Chapter 1
Workbook Activity
2

First Aid for Choking

A. Directions Look at the pictures below. The first one shows the universal distress signal for choking. The others illustrate first aid for choking. Review these actions in your textbook. Then practice them with a partner. Do not actually thrust when you practice the Heimlich maneuver or you may hurt the "victim."

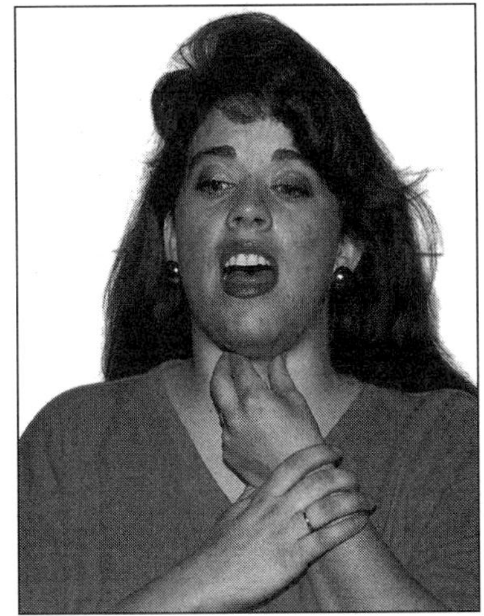

Universal distress signal for choking

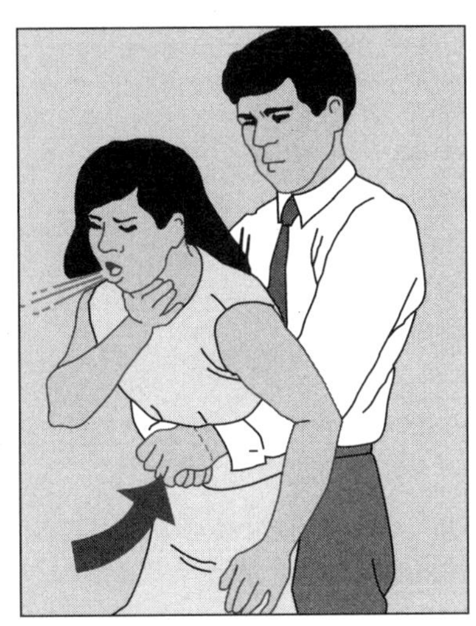

Heimlich maneuver

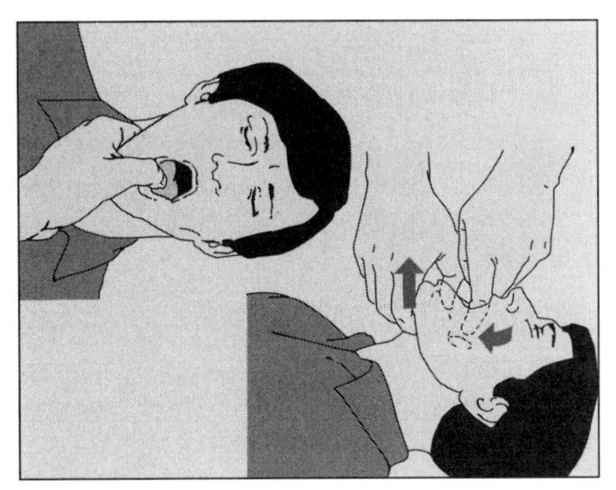

Finger sweep

B. Directions Answer the questions.

1) What does the universal distress signal for choking do?

____

2) What does the Heimlich maneuver do?

____

3) Why should you not pound on the back of a choking victim?

____

4) What other actions should you try if the Heimlich maneuver does not work?

____

5) What actions can you take if you are alone and choking?

____

Name Kyle Date 9/13 Period

Chapter 1
Workbook Activity
3

Ways to Remember First Aid Procedures

A. Directions The RICE formula is an easy way to remember first aid treatment for sprains. Each letter in RICE stands for a key word in the treatment. Underline the key word for each letter of RICE in the RICE formula below.

RICE Formula
R is for *rest*. Rest the limb or affected part.
I is for *ice*. Cover the affected part with ice to reduce swelling.
C is for *compression*. Wrap the injured part with an elastic bandage to compress the part and reduce swelling.
E is for *elevation*. Elevate, or raise, the injured part above the heart level if possible to prevent swelling and bleeding.

B. Directions Make up "RICE formulas" for two other first aid treatments. Choose the injury. Use your textbook to review the treatment for that injury. Then choose a word or series of letters that are easy to remember and that stand for key words in the treatment. Write the word and the treatment like the RICE formula. Exchange your paper with a classmate. Find and underline the key words on your partner's paper.

First Aid for ______________________

____

____

____

____

____

First Aid for ______________________

____

____

____

____

____

Name _______________ Date _______ Period _______

Chapter 1

Workbook Activity 4

Cardiovascular Disease

Directions The patient described below has just had a mild heart attack and is in the hospital. Read the patient's personal history. Then pretend you are the doctor. Write your recommendations and answers to the patient's questions on the lines below.

Patient: John

Age: 72

Gender: Male

Race: African-American

Personal habits: Smokes two packs of cigarettes daily. Enjoys foods high in fat and cholesterol.

Medical history: Has not seen a doctor in the last 15 years. Occasionally has severe chest pains.

Family history: Mother had a stroke when she was 61 years old.

Patient: I was surprised to find out I had a heart attack. Why me?

1) Doctor's response:

____

____

____

Patient: Are there symptoms or warnings I might have missed that signaled a heart attack was on the way?

2) Doctor's response:

____

____

____

Patient: Will I have to change my lifestyle? What can I do to overcome my risk factors for another attack?

3) Doctor's response:

____

____

____

Name _______________ Date _______ Period _______

Chapter 1
Workbook Activity 5

Causes of Disease

A. Directions Read each sentence below. Decide what most likely caused the disease. On each blank, write I for infection, B for behavior, or E for environment.

_____ **1)** Karin was hospitalized with lead poisoning.

_____ **2)** Claude's heart attack was a result of too much cholesterol in his diet.

_____ **3)** Everyone in the Jackson family got the flu in the same week.

_____ **4)** Theo developed a serious bone condition because he ate very little healthy food.

_____ **5)** Sally's foot became inflamed after she stepped on a nail.

_____ **6)** The children had breathing problems because their parents smoked.

_____ **7)** The germ in the drinking water affected the whole neighborhood.

_____ **8)** It seemed that Daryl was always sick, maybe because he was always sharing his drinking glass with others.

_____ **9)** Many people were taken to the emergency room when the chemical plant leaked gases into the air.

_____ **10)** Everyone at the party got food poisoning.

B. Directions Think about your personal health practices. On the lines below, list the things you could do to prevent getting an infectious disease such as a cold.

____

____

____

Name Date Period

Chapter 1
Workbook Activity 6

Getting the Most from Your Doctor's Appointment

A. Directions Your appointment gives you the opportunity to ask the doctor questions and gather information about your health. Simple advance preparation will help you make the most of your doctor's appointment.

Think of an illness or ailment you have had. Or think of an illness or ailment someone you know has had. Write down information about that illness or ailment that you would tell a doctor. You might include symptoms, when the illness started, and how you currently feel. Then write down questions you would ask the doctor.

1) Illness or ailment

____

2) Information to give the doctor

____

____

____

3) Questions to ask the doctor

____

____

____

____

____

B. Directions Answer the questions.

1) Why is it important to tell the doctor everything you can about how you are feeling?

____

____

2) Why is it important to ask the doctor questions and understand the answers?

____

____

Name Date Period

Chapter 1
Workbook Activity
7

Caring for Your Teeth

A. Directions Review the steps listed here for flossing teeth. Then follow the steps to practice flossing your teeth.

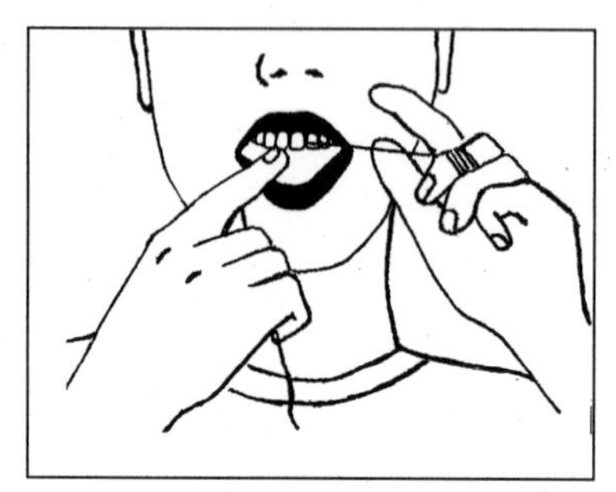

Length of floss with some of it wrapped around middle finger.

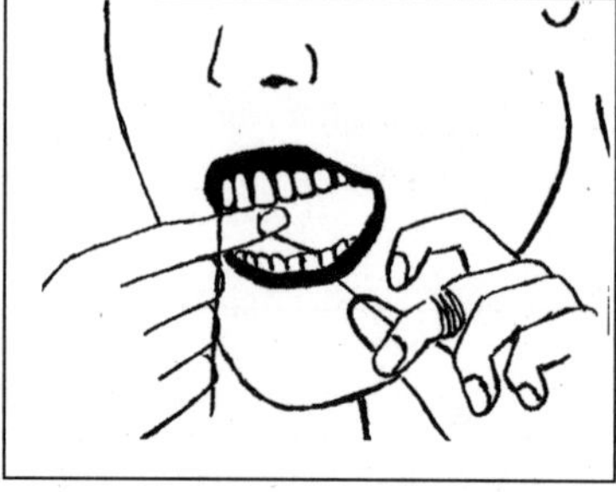

Floss between two teeth, moving up and down against sides of teeth.

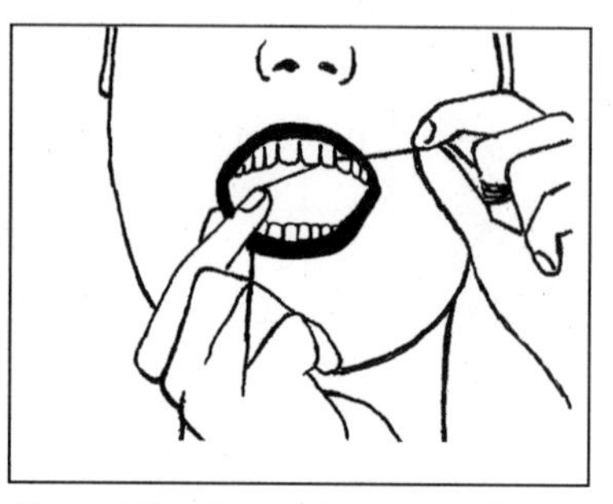

Floss sliding between gum and tooth with floss bent in C shape.

Flossing Steps

1) Break off about 18 inches of floss. Wrap some of it loosely around a middle finger.

2) Use a gentle sawing motion to slide the floss between teeth. Use a clean part of the floss for each tooth.

3) Slide the floss between the tooth and gum. Bend the floss toward one tooth to form a C shape. Scrape the side of each tooth gently with the floss.

4) Use a mirror so you can see what you are doing.

5) Wash your hands after you floss to get rid of germs.

B. Directions Flossing may take ten minutes to do. Do you think it's worth the time and effort? Explain your answer.

____

____

Name Date Period

Chapter 1
Workbook Activity
8

Learning to Read Prescription Labels

Directions Refer to the prescription label that appears here to answer the questions.

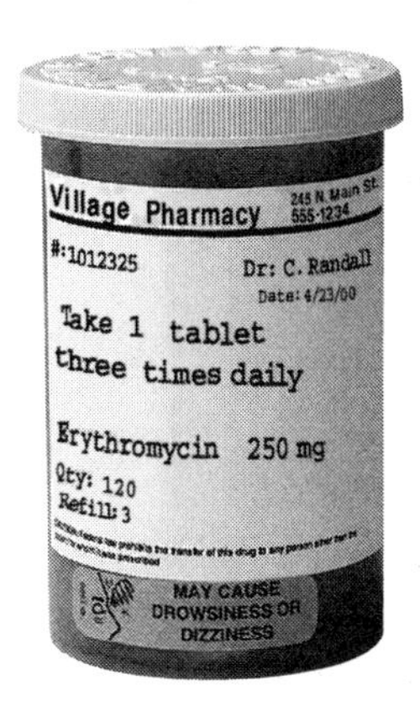

1) What is the name of this medicine?

____

2) Who is the doctor who prescribed it?

____

3) What is the prescription number?

____

4) Where was this prescription filled?

____

5) When was it filled?

____

6) How many tablets are in the bottle?

____

7) How often should the patient take a tablet?

____

8) How many times can the prescription be refilled?

____

9) How long will the bottle of pills last if taken as directed?

____

10) When should the prescription be refilled?

____

Name Date Period

Ways to Say No

A. Directions Here are some ways to say *no* when someone is trying to get you to use drugs or do something else you know is wrong. Circle the ones that would work best for you.

Ways to Say No

1) "No, thanks."

2) "No way—my family would kill me!"

3) "No way—the teacher would kill me!"

4) "I gave that up."

5) "I promised my family I wouldn't do that."

6) "I don't want to. But thanks anyway."

7) "I don't want to. End of discussion."

8) "I don't want to, and I can't believe you want to get into that kind of stuff."

9) "My mind is made up."

10) "I'm not interested."

11) "I make my own decisions."

12) "If I have to do that to be your friend, I guess I'll have to get a new friend."

13) "I'll pass."

14) "I like me the way I am."

15) "I don't need any."

16) "I'd rather save my brain for other things."

17) "I don't want to ruin my life."

18) "I'm allergic to that stuff."

19) "Who needs it."

20) "It's not for me."

21) "I've got all the great feelings I need."

22) "I'm not into that."

23) "No, I've got things to do."

24) "I'm trying to solve problems, not make more."

25) "I have a different opinion."

26) "I don't like people on drugs."

27) "I don't take those kinds of chances."

28) "I don't need that stuff to have fun."

29) "I can be spacey enough as it is."

30) "I said I wasn't interested. Now leave me alone."

31) "Are you crazy?"

32) "No!"

Name Date Period

Ways to Say No, continued

B. Directions Choose five of the ways to say *no* that would be easiest for you to use. Write the five ways and explain why they would be the easiest ones for you to use.

1) ______________________________

____

2) ______________________________

____

3) ______________________________

____

4) ______________________________

____

5) ______________________________

____

C. Directions Using your own words and ideas, write five more ways to say *no* that you could use.

1) ______________________________

2) ______________________________

3) ______________________________

4) ______________________________

5) ______________________________

D. Directions Interview three people to find out how they say *no*. Write the information each person shares with you below.

1) ______________________________

2) ______________________________

3) ______________________________

Name Date Period

Chapter 2
Workbook Activity
10

Search the Internet

A. Directions Read over the directions for conducting an Internet search on page 59 of your textbook. Then follow the directions to search for apartment rentals in your town. Answer the questions below about your search.

1) What search words did you use?

___

___

___

2) How many sites did you visit?

___

3) List the sites you visited.

___

___

4) What kind of information did you find at each site?

___

___

___

B. Directions Suppose you were very interested in one apartment listed online. Write on the lines below what you would do next to make this apartment your new home.

___

___

___

Name Date Period

Chapter 2
Workbook Activity 11

Following Label Directions

Directions Two fictional cleaning products appear here. Read the label on each product. Then answer the questions.

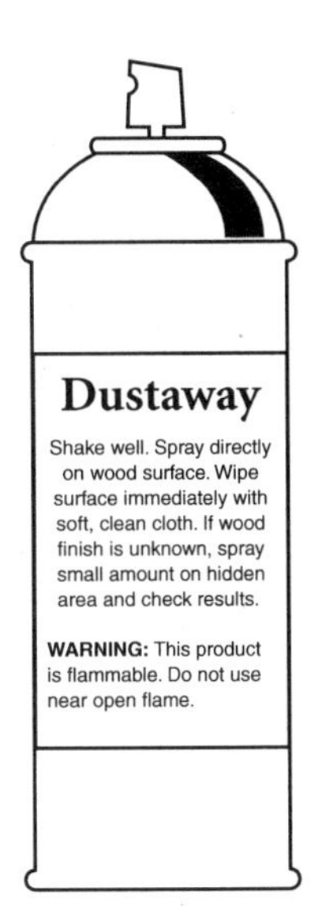

1) Which cleaner would you use to clean the bathroom mirror?

____

2) Which cleaner would you use to polish a wood table?

____

3) Can you use the same kind of cloth with both cleaners? Explain your answer.

____

4) Would it be wise to use Dustaway in the kitchen when cooking on a gas stove? Explain your answer.

____

5) Name three items you could clean with Dustaway and three items you could clean with Shiny Brite.

Dustaway	Shiny Brite
____________	____________
____________	____________
____________	____________

Name Date Period

Chapter 2
Workbook Activity
12

Reading a Utility Bill

Directions Study the utility bill shown below and then answer the following questions.

ZLX
Power Company

Your Account Number	Date Due	Please Pay	Amount Enclosed
145-32-000	9/12/00	$164.46	

Please Return This Portion
With Your Payment To:

P.O. BOX 1190
MPLS, MN 55768

SUSAN MANN
987045 ROLLING LANE
ROSEVILLE, MN 55113

X907890008799XXXXXXXXXYYYZZZZ0000000

Detach and Retain This Portion For Your Records

Current Charges

Electric Charges Usage Period: 7/15/00 to 8/16/00		
Residential - Underground	**32 Days**	
Basic Service Charge		$6.50
Energy Charge - 1,610 kwh @ $.073500		118.34
Subtotal		**$124.84**
State Tax @ 6.50%		$8.11
Total Amount		**$132.95**

Meter Reading Information
Meter xxx0009865433
Company Reading on 8/16........16466
Company Reading on 7/15........14856
Total 32 Days kwh 1610

Gas Charges Usage Period: 7/15/00 to 8/16/00		
Residential Service	32 Days	
Basic Service Charge		$6.50
Distribution Charge		5.74
Cost of Gas		17.35
Subtotal		**$29.59**
State Tax @ 6.50%		1.92
Total Amount		**$31.51**

Meter Reading Information
Meter #xxx9087788
Company Reading on 8/16........8586
Company Reading on 7/15........8556
Total 32 Days ccf 30

1) What was the billing period? List the dates.

____

2) How much electricity did the customer use during this billing period?

____

3) How much does the customer owe for gas usage?

____

4) What is the total amount of the bill?

____

5) When is the payment due?

____

Name Date Period

Chapter 2
Workbook Activity
13

Gathering Insurance Estimates

A. Directions Listed below are 10 steps to take when gathering insurance estimates. Put the steps in the correct order. Write 1 on the blank in front of the first thing you should do, 2 on the blank in front of the next thing to do, and so on.

_____Decide which policy you want and call the agent.

_____Write down questions to ask each agent.

_____Take notes and ask questions at the meetings with agents.

_____Make a list of three agents to contact.

_____Buy the policy and get a copy of it.

_____Determine the total value of the items on your list.

_____Set up appointments.

_____Make a videotape of your belongings to have a visual record.

_____Review your notes to compare the policies and their costs.

_____Make a list of all your belongings.

B. Directions Write the answer to these questions, using complete sentences.

1) What are some ways to find an insurance agent?

____

____

2) Whom would you ask to go with you to a meeting with an insurance agent? Why would you ask this person to come along?

____

____

Name Date Period

Chapter 2
Workbook Activity
14

Talking with Telemarketers

A. Directions With a classmate, role-play the following conversation between Pat and a telemarketer.

Telephone rings.

Pat: Hello.

Telemarketer: Hello, could I please speak with Pat Johnson?

Pat: This is Pat Johnson.

Telemarketer: Hello, Pat. I'm Sandy with XYZ Company. How are you doing this evening?

Pat: Fine, thank you.

Telemarketer: That's good. I'm calling to tell you about an exciting new offer we have right now at XYZ. I would like to offer you a credit card with a $10,000 credit limit. I can take your application over the phone. How does that sound?

Pat: Thank you, but I'm not interested.

Telemarketer: But Pat, this is the very best offer we've ever had. If you pass on this, you'll regret it later.

Pat: Thank you, but I'm really not interested. Good-bye.

Telemarketer: Thank you for your time. Good-bye.

B. Directions Write the answer to these questions, using complete sentences.

1) Why was Pat pleasant to the telemarketer?

____

2) Did Pat give out any personal information?

____

3) What could Pat have done if the telemarketer still tried to talk him into applying for the credit card?

____

Name Date Period

Chapter 2
Workbook Activity 15

Reading Clothing Care Labels

Directions Look at the clothing care labels shown here. Notice the symbols and their meanings. Answer the questions that follow.

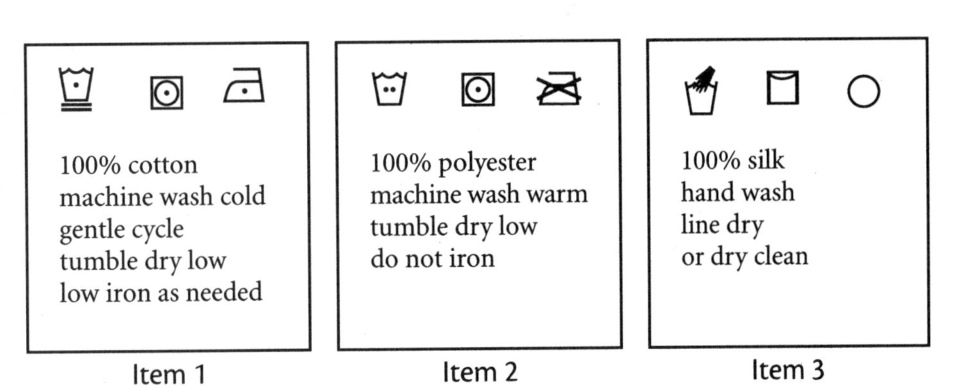

1) Which garment should not be washed in a washing machine?

____

2) Which garment is made of 100 percent polyester?

____

3) How should you set a washing machine for Item 1?

____

4) Should Items 1 and 2 be dried at the same temperature? Explain your answer.

____

5) Which items can be ironed with a warm iron?

____

6) What could happen to Item 3 if it was put in a clothes dryer?

____

7) What are two ways to clean Item 3?

____

8) What might happen to Item 1 if it was washed in warm water?

____

Name ____________________ Date ________ Period ________

Chapter 3
Workbook Activity 16

Home Safety

The message on your answering machine or voice mail should give only enough information to tell callers that they have dialed the correct number. You should not include personal information such as an address or the fact that you are away from home.

A. Directions Identify the information that should *not* be included in each message.

1) Hi, this is Marcy at (712) 432-9906. I'm gone for the weekend, but I'll call you back on Monday. Leave your message after the beep.

____

2) You've reached the Beckworth residence at 45 East Elm Street. Leave your message after you hear the beep.

____

3) Hello, this is Sandra. I use a wheelchair so it is hard for me to get to the phone. Call back again and let it ring at least six times.

____

4) Hello, this is Mrs. Harrison. I am elderly and live alone, so I love getting messages. Leave yours after the beep.

____

5) Hi, you've reached John at (563) 201-7234. Leave a message after the beep. I travel a lot for my business, so it might be a couple of days before I return your call.

____

6) Hi, this is the Clark residence at (601) 295-1103. If this is Susan calling, will you feed the cat while we are gone next week?

____

B. Directions Fill in the blanks to create your own answering machine message.

Hello, you have reached __________ at __________. I am sorry I can't talk to you right now. Please leave a message after the beep. I will return your call as soon as possible.

C. Directions Some messages include only the telephone number, but no name. Other messages include the name, but not the telephone number. Do you think you should use your name, your telephone number, or both? Give reasons for your opinion.

I think you should use ______________________________ because

____

____

____

Name Date Period

Chapter 3
Workbook Activity 17

Getting Help When You Are Away from Home

Directions Imagine you are present at each of these situations. You call for help on a cell phone. List the facts you would give in your phone call.

1) A woman is pushed to the ground and her purse is stolen.

____

____

2) A car running a red light hits and injures a person on a bicycle.

____

____

3) A person running to catch a bus slips and falls on the ice.

____

____

4) You are skating on a sidewalk and fall. You think your leg is broken.

____

____

5) You are in a meeting at work when a coworker suddenly clutches his chest and slumps over.

____

____

Name Date Period

Chapter 3

Workbook Activity 18

Recognizing Road Signs

A. Directions Road traffic signs have different shapes. Each shape has a different meaning. Octagons mean stop. A tall rectangle tells you about laws you must obey. A triangle means yield, or let others use the intersection before you. A diamond is a warning. A pentagon means a school or school crossing is nearby. A round sign with an X means a railroad crossing is ahead. Write the sign shape you think matches each meaning below.

_____________ **1)** There's a curving road ahead.

_____________ **2)** Watch out for children because a school is nearby.

_____________ **3)** A railroad crossing is ahead.

_____________ **4)** Come to a complete stop.

_____________ **5)** The road curves sharply up ahead, so slow down.

_____________ **6)** Yield the right-of-way to approaching cars.

_____________ **7)** The speed limit is 40 miles per hour.

_____________ **8)** You cannot park here at any time.

_____________ **9)** The street will be slippery when wet.

_____________ **10)** No left turns are allowed.

B. Directions The colors of road signs also provide information. In general, signs that tell you to do something are red, black, or white. Warning signs are yellow. Signs for construction or detours are orange. Highway signs are green. Service signs are blue. For each meaning listed below, write the most likely color for the sign.

R = red, BL/W = black and white, Y = yellow, O = orange, G = green, B = blue

_____ **1)** There is a rest area ahead with a telephone.

_____ **2)** Come to a complete stop.

_____ **3)** It is two miles until the next exit.

_____ **4)** This is a one-way street.

_____ **5)** There is a curved road ahead.

Name Date Period

Chapter 3

Workbook Activity 19

More Pedestrian Safety

A. Directions Choose the safest action for each situation by circling the letter.

1) You come to an intersection as the "Walk" sign starts to flash.
- **(a)** Run across the street.
- **(b)** Wait until the walk sign cycles and comes on again.
- **(c)** Cross in the middle of the street.
- **(d)** Wait for other people to cross the street with you.

2) You are halfway through an intersection as the "Walk" sign starts to flash.
- **(a)** Walk quickly across the remainder of the intersection.
- **(b)** Run back to where you started.
- **(c)** Stop and wait for the sign to change.
- **(d)** Wait until the sign says "Don't Walk."

3) You run out of gas on a busy street during the day. A gas station is one block away.
- **(a)** Ask a stranger to buy gas for you.
- **(b)** Ask some people to push your car to the gas station.
- **(c)** Lock your car and walk down to a gas station.
- **(d)** Honk your horn to attract attention.

4) You are riding in a taxi cab and reach your destination.
- **(a)** Always exit on the driver's side.
- **(b)** Always exit on the right side.
- **(c)** Exit on the side next to the curb.
- **(d)** Pay the driver before you exit.

5) You run out of gas on a deserted street at night.
- **(a)** Wave down a passing driver to get help.
- **(b)** Lock your car and walk to the nearest gas station.
- **(c)** Open the windows and play the radio loudly.
- **(d)** Lock your car and wait for help to arrive.

6) You have a long walk from a store to your car in a dark parking lot.
- **(a)** Ask a security guard to walk you to your car.
- **(b)** Run quickly to your car.
- **(c)** Stay in the shadows so you won't be seen.
- **(d)** Whistle or sing as you walk so you will sound brave.

B. Directions Use the space at the right to draw what is described in each statement. Use the back side if you need more space.

1) Sketch the intersection of two streets, Elm and Maple.

2) Draw a pedestrian crosswalk in the middle of the block on Elm.

3) Use a green marker to show three safe routes to cross a street.

4) Use a red marker to show three routes that are *not* safe.

Name Date Period

Chapter 3

Workbook Activity 20

Preparing for Natural Disasters

Directions To complete the worksheet, choose two natural disasters that might happen where you live. If your area is not subject to natural disasters, write *Fire* and *Power Outage* for your two choices. Write your responses for each disaster in the spaces provided.

	Natural Disaster #1:	Natural Disaster #2:
1) Where will you go if you are at home?		
2) Where will you go if you are at school?		
3) Where will you go if you are traveling to school or home from school?		
4) If you need help, who will you call? What is the person's telephone number?		
5) What emergency supplies should you have at home?		
6) Where at home will you keep the emergency supplies?		
7) How do you turn off the electricity in your home?		
8) How do you turn off the gas in your home?		
9) How will you get in touch with other family members?		
10) Are any of your family members elderly or disabled? If so, what kind of help might they need in the emergency?		

Name Date Period

Chapter 4
Workbook Activity
21

Who Has the Healthier Diet?

A. Directions Look at the two dinners that Allen and Lorie have eaten so far this week. Who do you think seems to have the healthier diet? Write your answer and your reasons on the lines below.

Who has the healthier diet and why?

____

____

____

____

Allen

Dinner 1
Salad with cucumbers, carrots, lettuce, spinach, and vinegar and olive oil dressing
Baked skinless chicken
Corn on the cob
Milk
Frozen yogurt

Dinner 2
Spaghetti with red sauce
Garlic bread
Fresh zucchini
Olive and celery salad
Lemonade
Lemon cookies

Lorie

Dinner 1
Salad with lettuce and thousand island dressing
Fried chicken
Mashed potatoes and gravy
Chocolate milk
Brownie with ice cream and hot fudge

Dinner 2
Cheese soup
Cheeseburger
French fries
Strawberry shake
Cheesecake

B. Directions Add another dinner to Allen's and Lorie's menus. Choose foods that you think Allen and Lorie are most likely to eat. Write your food choices in the lines below.

Allen's Dinner:

____

____

____

____

Lorie's Dinner:

____

____

____

____

Name Date Period

Chapter 4
Workbook Activity
22

A Nutrient Concept Map

A. Directions Create a concept map to compare the six essential nutrients. Fill in the blank spaces in the concept map that appears below. (Hint: Inner ovals = six essential nutrients; horizontal boxes = the functions the nutrients provide; outer ovals = food sources of nutrients)

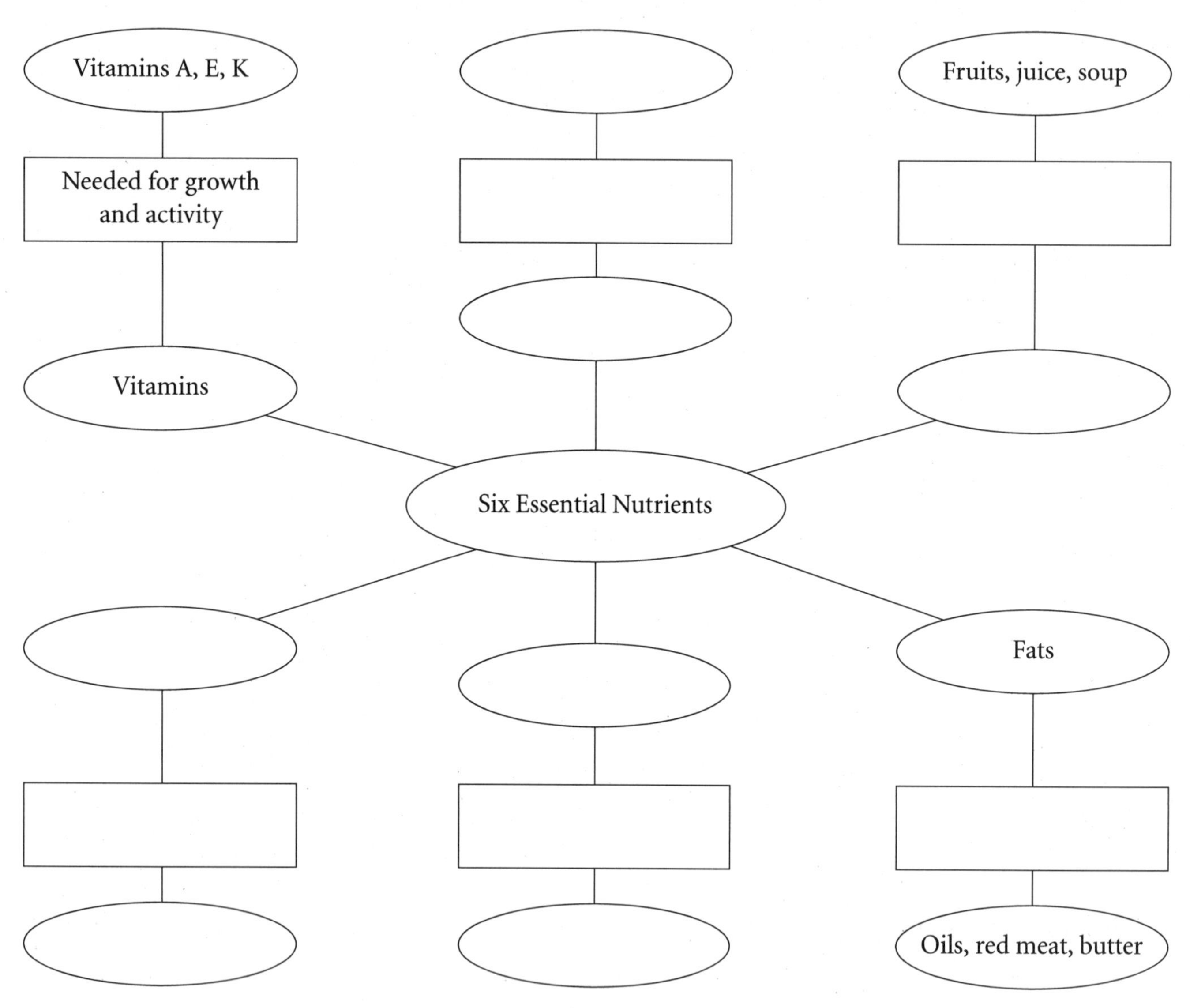

B. Directions Use your completed concept map to write two sentences about nutrients.

____

____

____

____

Name Date Period

Chapter 4
Workbook Activity
23

Some Healthy Recipes

A. Directions Here are some recipes for snacks that are healthy and taste good. Try making them at home.

Yogurt Shake
2 cups plain or vanilla yogurt
1/4 cup orange juice
1/2 cup frozen strawberries
banana
3 ice cubes

Place yogurt, orange juice, strawberries, and ice cubes in a blender. Slice the banana and add to the blender. Blend for 1 minute on medium speed. Stop the blender and stir the contents. Blend on medium speed again for 1 minute. Pour the shake into two glasses and serve.

English Muffin Pizzas
4 English muffins split in half
1 can (8 oz.) tomato sauce
1/4 pound grated mozzarella cheese
grated Parmesan cheese
1/2 teaspoon basil
1/2 teaspoon oregano
salami, pepperoni, mushrooms, or other toppings

Preheat the oven to 400°. Place the English muffins on a cookie sheet. Stir the tomato sauce, basil, and oregano in a small bowl. Spread one or two spoonfuls of sauce on each muffin half. Add some toppings. Sprinkle mozzarella cheese on each muffin. Bake 15-20 minutes or until cheese melts to golden brown. Before eating, sprinkle with Parmesan cheese if you wish.

B. Directions After reading the recipes, answer these questions.

1) Why is each recipe considered healthy?

____

____

____

2) How might you alter each recipe to change the flavor but still keep it healthy?

____

____

____

Name Date Period

Chapter 4
Workbook Activity 24

Maximum Heart Rate and Exercise

Directions How long should you exercise to improve your cardiovascular fitness? Find out by doing the following test.

1) Figure out your general maximum heart rate by subtracting your age from 220.
2) Do an aerobic exercise for at least ten minutes.
3) Immediately take your pulse for ten seconds. Find your pulse by placing your first two right fingers on the inside of your left wrist. You should feel a thump, or pulse, against your fingers. One thump is one heartbeat. Use a watch with a second hand to count the number of heartbeats in ten seconds. Multiply this number by six to get your exercising heart rate for one minute.
4) Divide your exercising heart rate by your maximum heart rate.
5) Multiply the result by 100 to determine the percent of maximum heart rate used.
6) Look at the chart below to find the number of minutes of exercise you need to do three to six days a week.

If your maximum heart rate is:	You can exercise for:
50 percent	45-52 minutes
55 percent	37-45 minutes
60 percent	30-37 minutes
65 percent	25-30 minutes
70 percent	20-25 minutes
75 percent	15-20 minutes

Here's an example for a 17-year-old with a heart rate of 120 after doing an aerobic exercise for ten minutes.

$220 - 17 = 203$

$20 \times 6 = 120$

$120 \div 203 = 0.59$

$0.59 \times 100 = 59$ percent

The person should probably exercise at this pace for about 30 to 37 minutes three to six times a week.

Name Date Period

Chapter 4
Workbook Activity
25

Ways to Relieve Stress

A. Directions Here are some ways to cope with problems in life and relieve stress. Read through the list. Then write down three ways you can think of to cope with problems and stress.

Methods for Coping with Problems and Stress

- Sit or lie down in a quiet place. Take several deep breaths. Breathe in through your nose and out through your mouth.
- Stretch your muscles to relieve tension.
- Do exercises or other physical activity.
- Identify the cause of the stress. For example, if you are angry, figure out what is making you angry.
- Take one thing at a time. You may have several problems piling up. Decide which ones you can handle now and which ones you can handle later.
- List several ways to solve your problems. Consider the results of each way, then choose the best.
- Accept what you cannot change. For example, if you did something in the past that causes you stress, accept that you cannot change the past. However, you can learn from mistakes and change your behavior.
- Think positively. Keep an "I can" attitude. Instead of viewing a situation as a problem, look at it as a challenge.
- Avoid situations that you know are going to cause stress. For example, if you know that illegal drugs will be at a party, you can choose not to go to the party.
- Take responsibility. Do not count on wishful thinking or wait for others to solve your problems.

Three more ways to cope with problems and stress:

1) ______________________________

2) ______________________________

3) ______________________________

B. Directions Think of something that recently caused stress in your life. Did you try any of the methods listed here? If so, did they help? If you did not use any of the methods, which ones do you think might have helped relieve your stress? Write your thoughts on a separate sheet of paper.

Name Date Period

Chapter 5
Workbook Activity 26

Strengths and Weaknesses

A. Directions Pair up with a classmate and trade papers. List your classmate's strengths in the left column. Leave the *Weaknesses* column blank. Your classmate can do the same for you. When you are both finished, trade papers and read the *Strengths* list. Then fill in the *Weaknesses* column on your own paper. [Example: For Communication Skills under *Strengths*, you might write *good listener.*]

STRENGTHS

Communication Skills

____

____

Academic Skills

____

____

Social Skills

____

____

WEAKNESSES

Communication Skills

____

____

Academic Skills

____

____

Social Skills

____

____

B. Directions Answer the questions.

1) How accurate was your classmate in identifying your strengths?

____

2) How accurate were you in identifying your weaknesses?

____

3) What did you learn about the way others see you?

____

____

Name Date Period

Chapter 5
Workbook Activity 27

Some Indicators of Emotionally Healthy People

A. Directions Write the word or words in parentheses that correctly complete each statement.

Emotionally healthy people:

1) know when to ______________ behaviors that aren't working.
(continue, change, use)

2) learn from successes, ______________, and mistakes.
(TV ads, experiences, emotions)

3) ______________ after something goes wrong.
(try again, quit, flip out)

4) face and overcome ______________.
(successes, disadvantages, happiness)

5) develop ______________ that guide their decision making.
(nerves, excuses, values)

6) set goals that are ______________ and reachable.
(easy, challenging, extremely difficult)

7) think about how their ______________ cause them stress.
(actions, relaxation, dreams)

8) have ______________ themselves and their abilities.
(questions about, displeasure for, faith in)

9) replace pessimistic thinking with ______________.
(doubts, questions, positive thoughts)

10) accept that they are ______________.
(always right, not perfect, very popular)

B. Directions Pick two statements from the list above that focus on things you would like to improve. Describe the actions you could take to improve in these areas.

____

____

____

____

Name Date Period

Chapter 5
Workbook Activity
28

Rate Your Self-Esteem

Directions Answer the questions.

1) Write five personal qualities that make you feel good about yourself.

______________ ______________ ______________ ______________ ______________

2) How would you describe your self-esteem?

____

____

3) Think about the last time you tried something new. Did you approach the situation with hope for success? Or were you afraid of failing? Explain your answer.

____

____

____

4) How do your feelings affect your self-esteem?

____

____

5) Do you ever feel lonely, shy, or self-conscious? How might these feelings increase your risk for drug or alcohol use?

____

____

____

Name ________ Date ________ Period ________

Chapter 5
Workbook Activity 29

Being Assertive

A. Directions Assertiveness is a form of communication. Assertive people know how to clearly express their feelings, needs, values, and beliefs. An assertive speaker uses words and body language to send a clear message to listeners. Read the following statements and check the ones that describe assertive communication.

____ Confident tone of voice
____ Look away from the listener
____ Unsure speech
____ Face the listener
____ Use "I" statements
____ Yell at the listener
____ Poor posture
____ Make direct eye contact
____ Smile at the listener
____ Use statements that put the listener down
____ Use simple statements
____ Serious facial expression

B. Directions Answer the questions using complete sentences.

1) Your best friend invites you to a drinking party with some older students. How would you respond in an assertive way?

____

____

2) Two classmates are making fun of a younger student. They urge you to join them. How would you respond in an assertive way?

____

____

3) You are waiting to return something you bought and it's your turn next. One woman is working the busy returns counter. Suddenly another worker joins her. The new worker asks the crowd, "Who's next?" How would you respond in an assertive way?

____

____

4) Your phone rings. You answer it and hear a telemarketer on the other end. He offers you a new credit card. You don't want a new credit card. How would you respond in an assertive way?

____

____

5) A stranger knocks on your door. She asks for a contribution to a well-known cause. Although the cause is legitimate, you are not able to contribute. How would you respond in an assertive way?

____

____

Name Date Period

Chapter 6
Workbook Activity 30

Paying with Cash

Directions Answer the questions.

1) Joe bought a pair of socks that cost $6.58. He gave the store clerk a $10 bill. What was his change?

____

2) Susan bought hand lotion that cost $2.33. She gave the clerk a $20 bill. What was her change?

____

3) Lee bought a pair of jeans that cost $39.98. He gave the clerk one $20 bill and three $10 bills. What was his change?

____

4) Latrice bought a book that cost $18.99. She gave the clerk a $50 bill. What was her change?

____

5) Darryl bought a videotape that cost $13.36. He gave the clerk three $5 bills. What was his change?

____

6) Ona bought a sweater that cost $58.22. She gave the clerk one $20 bill and four $10 bills. What was her change?

____

7) Max bought shaving cream that cost $3.28. He gave the clerk a $10 bill. What was his change?

____

8) Grace bought a suitcase that cost $129.33. She gave the clerk seven $20 bills. What was her change?

____

9) James bought a bottle of water and a pack of gum for $1.52. He gave the clerk a $5 bill. What was his change?

____

10) Helen bought a vase that cost $29.99. She gave the clerk two $20 bills. What was her change?

____

Name Date Period

Chapter 6
Workbook Activity 31

Budgeting

Directions Study the budget shown here. Use it to answer the questions.

Monthly Budget

Income	
Job	$1,812.00
Expenses	
Rent	$600.00
Car payment	115.00
Car insurance	85.00
Health insurance	77.00
Credit card payment	100.00
Electric	50.00
Phone	48.00
Water	30.00
Food	400.00
Gas	42.00
Clothing	40.00
Recreation	75.00
Vacation	50.00
Savings	100.00
TOTAL Expenses	$1,812.00
GRAND TOTAL	$0.00

1) Which expenses shown on the budget must be paid in full each month?

____

____

2) Which expenses shown on the budget can be adjusted if necessary?

____

____

3) Suppose you have to buy a wedding gift for your cousin. From which category or categories on your budget might you cut spending to afford the gift?

____

____

4) How much of the budget is set aside for savings? About what percentage of the budget is this?

____

____

5) What categories in this budget have costs that probably will not change from month to month?

____

____

Name Date Period

Chapter 6

Workbook Activity 32

Using Deposit and Withdrawal Slips

Directions Practice filling out savings deposit and withdrawal slips using the information below.

1) You received a check for $100. You want to put all of it into your savings account. Fill out the deposit slip.

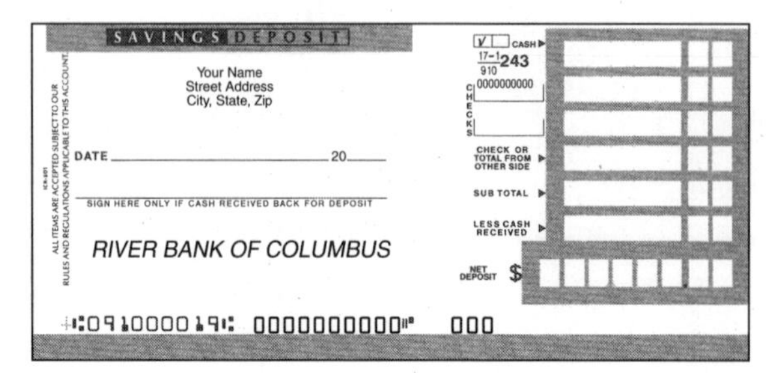

SAVINGS DEPOSIT

Your Name
Street Address
City, State, Zip

DATE ______________ 20____

SIGN HERE ONLY IF CASH RECEIVED BACK FOR DEPOSIT

RIVER BANK OF COLUMBUS

ALL ITEMS ARE ACCEPTED SUBJECT TO OUR RULES AND REGULATIONS APPLICABLE TO THIS ACCOUNT

CASH
17-1/910 243
0000000000
CHECKS
CHECK OR TOTAL FROM OTHER SIDE
SUB TOTAL
LESS CASH RECEIVED
NET DEPOSIT $

⑆0910000191⑆ 0000000000⑈ 000

2) You want to withdraw $25 from your savings account. Fill out the withdrawal slip.

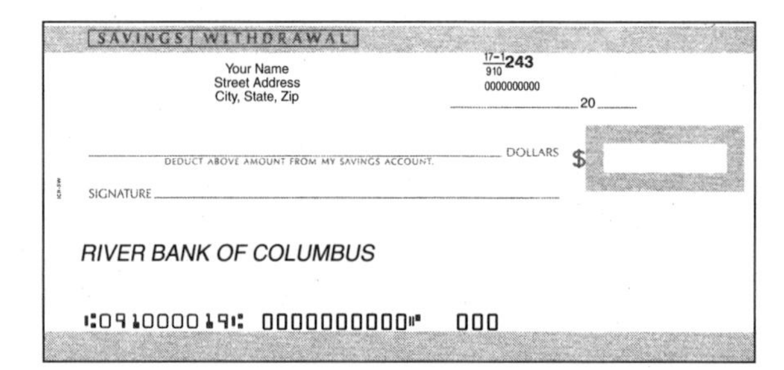

SAVINGS WITHDRAWAL

Your Name
Street Address
City, State, Zip

17-1/910 243
0000000000

______________ 20____

______________ DOLLARS $

DEDUCT ABOVE AMOUNT FROM MY SAVINGS ACCOUNT.

SIGNATURE ______________

RIVER BANK OF COLUMBUS

⑆0910000191⑆ 0000000000⑈ 000

3) You received a check for $200. You want to deposit $150 into your savings account and get $50 cash. Fill out the deposit slip.

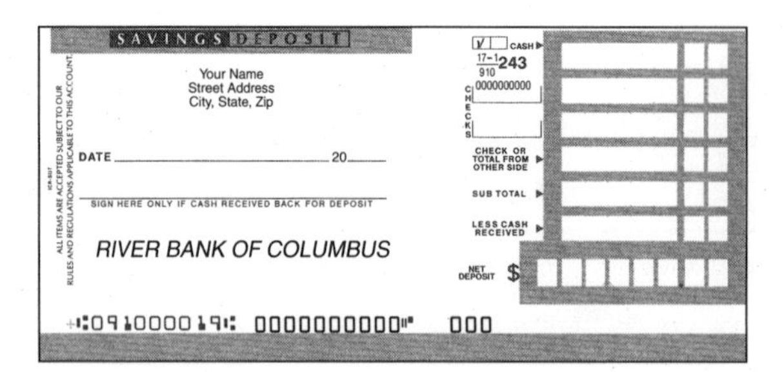

SAVINGS DEPOSIT

Your Name
Street Address
City, State, Zip

DATE ______________ 20____

SIGN HERE ONLY IF CASH RECEIVED BACK FOR DEPOSIT

RIVER BANK OF COLUMBUS

ALL ITEMS ARE ACCEPTED SUBJECT TO OUR RULES AND REGULATIONS APPLICABLE TO THIS ACCOUNT

CASH
17-1/910 243
0000000000
CHECKS
CHECK OR TOTAL FROM OTHER SIDE
SUB TOTAL
LESS CASH RECEIVED
NET DEPOSIT $

⑆0910000191⑆ 0000000000⑈ 000

4) Should you sign the withdrawal slip in item #2 above? Explain your answer.

____

5) Do you need to sign the deposit slip in item #3? Explain your answer.

____

Name Date Period

Chapter 6
Workbook Activity
33

Using an ATM

A. Directions Place a check next to each banking task that you can do at an ATM machine.

____ Buy savings bonds

____ Deposit money in a savings account

____ Open a checking account

____ Transfer money between accounts

____ Open a savings account

____ Withdraw money from an account

____ Deposit money in a checking account

____ Put something in a safe deposit box

____ Check an account balance

B. Directions Write the correct word or words on the blank to complete each sentence.

1) ATM stands for automated ______________ machine.

2) To use an ATM, you need an ATM ______________.

3) To use an ATM, you also need a PIN, or personal ______________ number.

4) To protect yourself, you should never let anyone see you input your ______________.

C. Directions Circle the best answer to each question.

1) What is the correct order of things to do when using an ATM?

(a) Input PIN. Answer questions on screen. Insert ATM card.

(b) Answer questions on screen. Insert ATM card. Input PIN.

(c) Insert ATM card. Input PIN. Answer questions on screen.

2) How much do banks usually charge for the use of an ATM?

(a) $50 per year

(b) $1 to $2 each time you use it

(c) $10 per month

Name Date Period

Chapter 6

Workbook Activity 34

Identifying Parts of a Paycheck Stub

Directions Study the paycheck stub shown here. Then answer the questions.

SUNSHINE REAL ESTATE

CHECK NO: 010238
CHECK DATE: 11/24/00
PERIOD ENDING: 11/24/00
PAY FREQUENCY: SEMIMONTHLY

JENNIFER PEREZ

ID NUMBER: 01234
BASE RATE: 7.00/HOUR

IMPORTANT MESSAGE

HOURS AND EARNINGS

DESCRIPTION	CURRENT HOURS	CURRENT EARNINGS	Y-T-D HOURS	Y-T-D EARNINGS
HOURLY	32.00	224.00	147.25	1030.75
TOTAL HOURS/EARNINGS	32.00	224.00	147.25	1030.75

TAXES AND DEDUCTIONS

DESCRIPTION	CURRENT AMOUNT	Y-T-D AMOUNT
SO SEC TAX (FICA)	13.89	63.91
CITY TAX	3.25	14.95
FED INC TAX	17.04	74.98
STATE TAX	6.72	30.93
TOTAL TAXES	40.90	184.77

	GROSS	PRE-TAX	TAXABLE WAGES	LESS TAXES	LESS DED	NET PAY
CURRENT	224.00	.00	224.00	40.90	.00	183.10
Y-T-D	1030.75	.00	1030.75	184.77	.00	845.98

1) How many hours does this paycheck cover? ______________

2) How much of this check went to FICA? ______________

3) How much went to state taxes? ______________

4) How much went to local taxes? ______________

5) How much YTD has gone to FICA? ______________

6) How much YTD has gone to state taxes? ______________

7) How much YTD has gone to local taxes? ______________

8) What is the YTD gross? ______________

9) What is the YTD net? ______________

10) What percentage of this paycheck went to taxes? ______________

Name _______________ Date _______ Period _______

Chapter 6

Workbook Activity 35

Reading Credit Card Bills

Directions Study the credit card bill shown here. Then answer the questions.

Cards Are Us

Account Number
5329 0535 4900 0323

	Payment Due Date	*New Balance Total*
	9/12/00	$136.66
Cardholder Since	*Total Minimum Balance Due*	*Amount Enclosed*
1999	$15.00	$ _______

Make check payable to:

CARDS ARE US
P.O. BOX 1310
MPLS, MN 55355

SUSAN MANN
987045 ROLLING LANE
ROSEVILLE, MN 55113

X907890008799XXXXXXXXXYYYZZZZ0000000

Detach and Retain This Portion For Your Records

Account Number	*Credit Line*	*Cash or Credit Available*	*Days in Biling Cycle*	*Closing Date*	*Total Min Payment Due*	*Payment Due Date*
5329 0535 4900 0323	$2,500.00	$2,363.34	32	8/14/00	$15.00	9/12/00

Posting Date	Transaction Date	Reference Number	Card	Category	Transaction	**August 2000 Statement**	Charges	Credits (CR)
Payments and Credit								
7/27		7314	MC		Payment – Thank You			50.00 CR
Purchases and Adjustments								
7/15	7/14	3900	MC	C	Petscape	877/555-5555	38.48	
8/12	8/11	8222	MC	C	Petscape	877/555-5555	38.48	
	Total for Billing Cycle from 7/14/2000 through 8/14/2000						**$76.96**	**$50.00 CR**

SUMMARY OF TRANSACTIONS

Previous Balance	(-) Payments and Credits	(+) Cash Advances	(+) Purchases and Adjustments	(+) Periodic Rate FINANCE CHARGES	(+) Transaction Fee FINANCE CHARGES	(-) New Balance Total
$100.00	$50.00	$0.00	$76.96	$9.70	$0.00	$136.66

1) What is the payment due date? _______________

2) What is the new balance? _______________

3) What is the minimum payment due amount? _______________

4) What is the credit line on this card? _______________

5) What is the finance charge on the current balance? _______________

6) What is the cash or credit available amount? _______________

7) What is the previous month's balance? _______________

8) How much was charged to the card in the billing cycle? _______________

9) How much did the card holder pay the month before? _______________

10) Should the card holder pay the new balance total? Explain your answer.

____

Name Date Period

Chapter 6
Workbook Activity
36

Consumers Have Rights

Directions Here are some rights that all consumers have. Read the list of consumers' rights and then answer the questions.

- **The right to be safe.** You have a right to purchase goods that will not be harmful to you.
- **The right to make choices.** You have a right to choose from a variety of products at a variety of prices.
- **The right to be heard.** You have a right to get involved in the making of laws to protect consumers.
- **The right to get accurate information.** You have a right to receive truthful information about all products you buy.
- **The right to have problems solved.** You have a right to complain and you have a right to expect that your problems will be corrected.
- **The right to learn consumer skills.** You have a right to learn how to be a wise consumer.

1) What is a product you have seen advertised that you do not think would do what the advertiser promises?

____

2) Which consumer right do you think the product in question #1 violates?

____

3) Suppose you are returning a defective product to a store. Which consumer right are you exercising?

____

4) Suppose you are returning a product because you can buy it at a lower price at a competitor's store. Which consumer right are you exercising?

____

5) Write a brief letter to notify the manufacturer of a defective product. Keep the letter professional. Tell the manufacturer why you are dissatisfied. Tell the company what you would like to have happen (a credit or a refund).

____

____

____

____

Name ______ Date ______ Period ______

Chapter 6

Workbook Activity 37

Figuring Sales Tax

A. Directions Suppose sales tax in your state on most items is 6 percent. However, there is no sales tax on food or clothing. Figure out the sales tax and the total price for each item. Use a calculator.

1) Calculator $49

Sales tax ________

Total price ________

2) Loaf of bread $1.49

Sales tax ________

Total price ________

3) Book $16.99

Sales tax ________

Total price ________

4) Bicycle $289.50

Sales tax ________

Total price ________

5) Woman's suit $139.99

Sales tax ________

Total price ________

B. Directions Suppose sales tax in your state on most items is 8 percent. There is no sales tax on food. Figure out the sales tax and the total price for each item. Use a calculator.

1) Winter coat $99.99

Sales tax ________

Total price ________

2) Box of cereal $2.69

Sales tax ________

Total price ________

3) Computer software $549

Sales tax ________

Total price ________

4) Pair of jeans $27.99

Sales tax ________

Total price ________

5) One dozen eggs 89¢

Sales tax ________

Total price ________

Name Date Period

Chapter 6
Workbook Activity 38

Personal Savings Plan

A. Directions Saving for retirement takes some planning. You can start by making a savings plan for the year. Fill in the lines to show how you will divide your money. You may not be able to put money into all these retirement options. Pick those that will work best for you.

Yearly income ______________

Amount to put into a CD ______________

Amount to use to buy a savings bond ______________

Amount to put into an IRA ______________

Amount to put into a tax-deferred savings plan ______________

B. Directions Suppose your income doubles. How would you change the way you save your money? Fill in the lines to show a new savings plan.

Yearly income ______________

Amount to put into a CD ______________

Amount to use to buy a savings bond ______________

Amount to put into an IRA ______________

Amount to put into a tax-deferred savings plan ______________

Name Date Period

Chapter 7
Workbook Activity 39

Identifying Computer Hardware

A. Directions Five common pieces of computer hardware appear here. Can you identify them? Write the correct name of each piece on the line next to it.

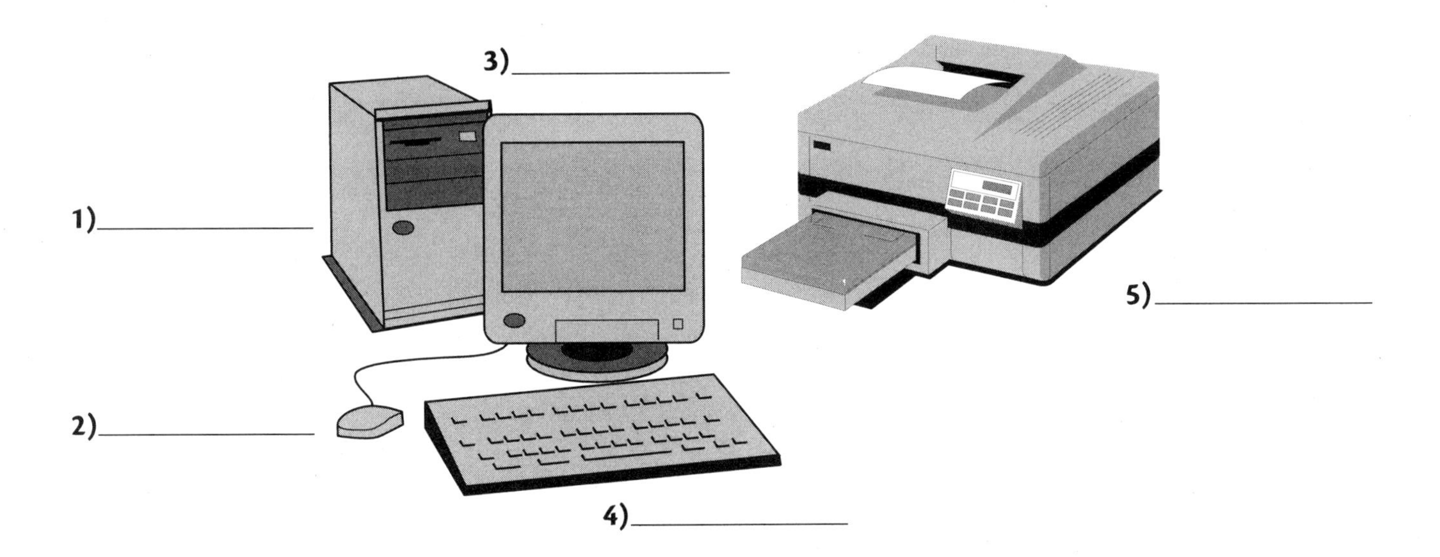

B. Directions Match each item on the left with the correct item on the right. Write the letter on the blank next to each numbered item.

____ **1)** computer base unit

____ **2)** keyboard

____ **3)** monitor

____ **4)** mouse

____ **5)** printer

a) You use this to select, or highlight, information.

b) It contains everything that runs the computer.

c) It prints copies of your work.

d) It displays information.

e) You use this to input information.

Name Date Period

Chapter 7
Workbook Activity
40

Creating Folders

A. Directions Listed here are eight steps you would follow to create a folder. Put the steps in the correct order. Write a number from 1 through 8 on the blank next to each step.

____ Type the name of the folder in the highlighted space.

____ Close the existing folder.

____ Click on *File.*

____ Scroll to *Folder* and click.

____ Click away from the *New Folder* icon.

____ Scroll down to *New.*

____ Open an existing folder.

____ Click on the *New Folder* icon and drag it outside the existing folder area.

B. Directions Fill in the blank to complete each sentence.

1) To move a file from one folder to another, first ______________ the folder that holds the file.

2) When you move a file, a copy of the file ______________ remain in the original folder.

Name ______________________ Date __________ Period __________

Chapter 7
Workbook Activity 41

Connecting to the Internet

A. Directions Choose the word from the Word Bank that correctly completes each sentence.

Word Bank

address	hard drive	Help	time
computers	shortcut	language	text

1) The Internet is a worldwide system of ______________ that connect to each other through telephone and cable lines.

2) Most Internet service providers base their fees on the amount of ______________ a customer spends on the Internet.

3) Computers on the Internet use a common ______________ to communicate.

4) A Web browser changes coded ______________ into a readable form.

5) When you bookmark a site, you create a ______________ to it.

6) Every Internet site has its own ______________ that starts with *http.*

7) Whenever you have a question about using the computer or the Internet, click on the ______________ command.

8) When you connect to a Web site, you log on to a ______________ on a remote computer network.

B. Directions You are shopping for an Internet service provider. You have made a list of five companies to call. Put a check next to each question you would ask.

____ 1) What is the monthly fee?

____ 2) Who owns the company?

____ 3) What features does the company offer?

____ 4) Is a deposit needed to begin service?

____ 5) Is the company local?

____ 6) Does the company provide software?

____ 7) Will the software work with any computer?

____ 8) How many employees does the company have?

____ 9) How soon can service begin?

____ 10) How often does the company bill its customers?

____ 11) Does the company require automatic payment by credit card?

____ 12) Do customers have to sign a contract?

Name Date Period

Chapter 7
Workbook Activity
42

Downloading from the Internet

A. Directions Write T if the statement is true. Write F if the statement is false.

____ **1)** When you download a file, you move a copy of it from one computer to another.

____ **2)** Everything on the Internet can be downloaded.

____ **3)** The downloading process is the same for all computers.

____ **4)** Many computers perform the download function as soon as you click on a file's icon or name.

____ **5)** A downloaded file can infect a computer with a virus.

____ **6)** An antivirus program prevents you from downloading files.

____ **7)** You own any document you download from the Internet.

____ **8)** It is possible to download an antivirus program from an Internet service provider.

____ **9)** When choosing an e-mail address, you should consider who you will be communicating with through e-mail.

____ **10)** An e-mail with an error in the *To* address will reach its intended destination.

B. Directions Rewrite each false statement from above to make it true. Use the lines below.

____

____

____

____

____

____

Name Date Period

Chapter 7
Workbook Activity
43

Writing E-mail

A. Directions Use the following information to write an e-mail message to a friend to arrange to get together. Use shortened words in your message if appropriate.

- Use a word or words that tell the main idea of the message.
- E-mail address of the person sending the message.
- E-mail address of the person receiving the message.
- Write the message in the form of a letter.

TO: ______________________________

FROM: ______________________________

SUBJECT: ______________________________

____

____

____

CLOSING ______________________________

B. Directions Now write an e-mail message to your supervisor about a work-related project or problem.

TO: ______________________________

FROM: ______________________________

SUBJECT: ______________________________

____

____

____

CLOSING ______________________________

Note: You can take this exercise a step further. If you have access to a computer and the Internet, practice writing, reading, and responding to e-mail.

Name ______________________ Date ________ Period ________

Chapter 7
Workbook Activity 44

Conducting a Search

A. Directions Choose the word from the Word Bank that correctly completes each sentence.

Word Bank

address	information	percent	rate
index	narrower	program	specific

1) The Internet contains a vast amount of ______________.

2) A search engine is a site that offers a(n) ______________ of other Internet sites.

3) The main screen of an Internet service provider's ______________ usually has a Search box.

4) The purpose of a search is to find a list of sites that contain ______________ information.

5) Generally, the more words you type into a Search box, the ______________ your search.

6) Some search engines ______________ the results of a search.

7) A site that is marked with 100 ______________ strongly matches the search words.

8) Most search results include each site's Internet ______________.

B. Directions What search word or words would you use to gather information on the following topics:

1) Music

____

____

2) Camping

____

____

Note: You can take this exercise a step further. If you have access to a computer and the Internet, try the search words you have chosen by entering them into a search engine.

Name Date Period

Chapter 8
Workbook Activity
45

"I" and "You" Messages

With an "I" message, you tell people how you feel about what they're doing or what effect they are having on you. The receiver of an "I" message is less likely to feel attacked. On the other hand, "you" messages communicate to other people that what they are doing is wrong. These messages usually sound critical or blaming, and the receiver often feels hurt, defensive, or angry.

Directions Some "you" messages appear here. On the line below each "you" message, rewrite the message to make it an "I" message.

1) "Hey! Your big head is blocking the TV. Move over!"

____

2) "If you cared at all for me, you'd go to the party with me."

____

3) "You always have to ride in the front seat. You're the rudest person I know."

____

4) "You say the nastiest things to everybody. No wonder no one can stand you."

____

5) "You're always pointing that stupid camera at me. Why don't you get a life?"

____

6) "You're such a blabbermouth!"

____

7) "How many times do I have to tell you this? Don't you have a brain in your head?"

____

8) "You're really mean to me. I don't make fun of your hair."

____

9) "You're always with your friends. You never spend time with me."

____

10) "Every time I see you, you're glued to that TV. Is that all you do all day?"

____

Name Date Period

Chapter 8
Workbook Activity 46

Responding to Rejection

Rejection hurts, but it is something everyone experiences now and then. Since occasional rejection can't be avoided, it's a good idea to practice healthy ways of dealing with it.

Directions Some ways to respond to rejection appear here. On the blank line next to each statement, write H if it is a healthy response to rejection or U if it is an unhealthy response.

_____ **1)** "You're such a jerk. I wouldn't want to be your friend anyway."

_____ **2)** "I'm sorry you feel that way."

_____ **3)** "I'm disappointed about not being invited to the party. Guess I'll have to find something else to do."

_____ **4)** "I'm so ugly, no one will ever like me."

_____ **5)** "Can we talk about it? I really like you, and I still want to be friends."

_____ **6)** "Yeah, well, drop dead yourself."

_____ **7)** "My 2-year-old brother is better company than you are. I don't want to see you anyway."

_____ **8)** "I feel good about my beliefs, and I won't give them up for you."

_____ **9)** "I tried hard to make our relationship work, but Cary broke up with me anyway. I'll never let myself care about anyone like that ever again. That way, I'm sure never to get hurt."

_____ **10)** "R.J. canceled a date with me for the third time. I'm so depressed. I think I'll call my uncle Alfonse. He always knows what to say to make me feel better."

Name Date Period

Chapter 8
Workbook Activity
47

Courteous Behavior

Directions Each sentence below describes a discourteous action. On the blank lines below each one, describe a way that the action could be done courteously.

1) Stanley cracked his gum throughout Reverend Allison's sermon.

____

____

2) Arthur finished his potato chips and threw the empty bag on the ground.

____

____

3) Calvin burped in class and when the other students looked at him, he pointed at Emily.

____

____

4) Emmett borrowed Reginald's sweatshirt and never returned it.

____

____

5) The invitation said dinner at 7:30 P.M. Sante showed up at 8:15 P.M.

____

____

Name Date Period

Chapter 8

Workbook Activity 48

Symptoms and Treatments of STDs

Directions The following terms relate to sexually transmitted diseases. Some are symptoms and some are treatments. Using the following terms, fill in the chart below. You will use some terms more than once.

a) pain when urinating
b) eye medicine for newborns
c) medicine to control symptoms
d) vaginal discharge
e) swollen testicles
f) discharge from urethra
g) medicine to ease pain
h) gradual blindness
i) dry cough
j) chills and fever
k) painful, small blisters
l) swollen lymph nodes
m) chancre
n) pelvic pain
o) night sweats
p) paralysis
q) antibiotic
r) "copper penny" rash
s) tumors
t) penicillin

	Some Symptoms	Treatments
AIDS		
Gonorrhea		
Genital Herpes		
Chlamydia		
Syphilis		

Name Date Period

Chapter 8

Workbook Activity 49

Create a Decision-Making Chart

Suppose you have won a shopping spree at either a clothing store or a music store. You can't do both, so you have to decide whether you would rather buy clothes or CDs. The reasons for your decision may seem silly, but are important. For example, you don't want your brother to borrow your CDs, so you might choose to buy clothes. Or maybe you want to practice some dance moves and you would like some new music. You can probably think of several other reasons to pick the clothing store or music store shopping spree.

Directions Follow the directions below to fill in the decision-making chart.

1) Your options are a shopping spree at a clothing store or a shopping spree at a music store.

2) Why would you choose each option? Think of three pluses for each option and write them in the middle column.

3) Why wouldn't you choose each option? Think of three minuses for each option and write them in the right-hand column.

Options	Pluses	Minuses
Option 1: Shopping spree at clothing store.	**1)**	**1)**
	2)	**2)**
	3)	**3)**
Option 2: Shopping spree at music store.	**1)**	**1)**
	2)	**2)**
	3)	**3)**

4) Evaluate the pluses and minuses for each option. Which shopping spree would you choose? Explain your answer.

Name ____________________ Date __________ Period __________

Chapter 8 — Workbook Activity 50

Create a To-Do List

A. Directions Think of five tasks that you need to complete in an average day. Write each task on the blank lines in the left-hand column. Then rank your tasks by numbering them in order of most important to least important. Most important = 1; least important = 5.

Task	Rank
1) ____________________	____________________
2) ____________________	____________________
3) ____________________	____________________
4) ____________________	____________________
5) ____________________	____________________

B. Directions On the blank line below, write down a long-term goal—that is, one that you would like to achieve in the next three to five years. Then list four tasks or steps you will need to complete to achieve your goal. Rank the four tasks or steps in the order you will need to complete them. Write the ranking number next to the task or step.

My long-term goal is:

____

I need to complete these steps to achieve my goal:

1) ____

2) ____

3) ____

4) ____

Name Date Period

Chapter 9
Workbook Activity
51

Recreational Activities

A. Directions List eight to 12 recreational activities you might like to do in your free time. First, review as many kinds of activities as you can. Start with the lists on pages 277 and 278 in your textbook. Use the library to find books on recreation and hobbies. Search the Internet using keywords such as *recreation* and *hobbies.*

______________ ______________ ______________ ______________

______________ ______________ ______________ ______________

______________ ______________ ______________ ______________

B. Directions Now choose your five favorite activities from the list you created. Write them in the first column below. In the other columns, list the materials/equipment and costs of the activities, and where and when you will do the activities.

Activity	Materials/Equipment	Costs	Where	When
1)				
2)				
3)				
4)				
5)				

C. Directions Answer the questions.

1) Which of these activities can you do with other people?

____

2) Would that make the activities more enjoyable? If so, how?

____

____

Name Date Period

Chapter 9
Workbook Activity
52

Traveler's Checklist

Directions Review each item in the checklist. See if you can add three more items to the list. Save the list to use the next time you travel.

- Collect information about your destination.
- Decide on travel dates. Find out the best time of year to go. Sometimes airline and hotel rates are lower if you stay past Saturday.
- Decide on transportation to your destination: car, bus, train, boat, or plane.
- Decide whether you need to rent a car at your destination.
- Let family members and close friends know about your trip.
- Arrange to have mail picked up or stopped while you are gone.
- Find out what the weather will be like and pack suitable clothes.
- Choose a route and alternate routes.
- If you are traveling in a group with more than one vehicle, decide when and where to meet others.
- If you are flying, find out if your hotel offers a free ride from the airport.
- Budget your money for the trip, both before and during the trip. Consider costs of transportation, food, lodging, sightseeing, and other entertainment. Keep track of expenses in a small notebook.
- Buy traveler's checks at the bank.
- Find out about exchange rates on money if you are traveling out of the country.
- Get a passport for traveling out of the country.
- ______________________________
- ______________________________
- ______________________________

Name ________ Date ________ Period ________

Chapter 9

Workbook Activity 53

Choosing a Candidate

A. Directions How do you decide to vote for one candidate over another? Here are some qualities that voters might consider when choosing a candidate. Put a check mark next to at least three qualities you think are important. On the blank lines, describe why each is important. Pick another quality you think is important. Write it on the last line and describe why it is important.

The candidate's

_____ **1)** stand on the issues

_____ **2)** personality

_____ **3)** leadership ability

_____ **4)** appearance

_____ **5)** experience

_____ **6)** intelligence

_____ **7)** honesty and integrity

_____ **8)** additional quality: ________________

These qualities are important because:

____

____

____

B. Directions Using a scale from 1 to 8, where 1 is very important and 8 is not important, rate each quality on the list. Add your quality on the last line and rank it.

The candidate's

_____ **1)** stand on the issues

_____ **2)** personality

_____ **3)** leadership ability

_____ **4)** appearance

_____ **5)** experience

_____ **6)** intelligence

_____ **7)** honesty and integrity

_____ **8)** additional quality: ________________

Name ______ Date ______ Period ______

Chapter 9

Workbook Activity 54

Community Laws

Directions Find out if your community has laws about the topics listed here. Check with the police department or city hall. Briefly describe the laws and the penalties for breaking them. List and describe any other laws your community has.

	Laws	Descriptions and Penalties
1)	Curfews	______
2)	Littering	______
3)	Pets on leashes	______
4)	Picking up after pets	______
5)	Jaywalking	______
6)	Parking on streets overnight	______
7)	Noise	______
8)	Spitting	______
9)	Keeping up property	______
10)	Speed limits on side streets	______
11)	______	______
12)	______	______

Name Date Period

Chapter 10
Workbook Activity
55

Self-Assessment Chart

Directions Write your interests, abilities, and values in the appropriate columns below. Read the following examples to help you get started.

Interests: things you like to do

Examples: business, accounting, math, history, sales, marketing, sports, science, politics, performing, electronics, adventure, animals

Abilities: things you have the ability to learn or to do well

Examples: math computation, high energy, high motivation, relating to others, listening skills, coordination, communication skills, speed, abstract reasoning, writing skills, patience, persistence, friendliness

Values: things that are important to you

Examples: job security, making a good income, having short working hours, variety in work, moving from place to place, working with others, helping others, having status or prestige, being independent, having responsibility, being part of a team, being creative

	My Interests	My Abilities	My Values
1)			
2)			
3)			
4)			
5)			
6)			
7)			
8)			
9)			
10)			

Name Date Period

Chapter 10

Workbook Activity 56

Identify Your Ideal Job

Directions Create a description of your ideal job by filling in the information below.

Job title

___

Responsibilities

___

___

Hours

___

Pay

___

Location

___

Working conditions

___

___

These working conditions are perfect for me because

___

The people I work with are great because

___

My ideal boss will be

___

Values that the job fulfills

___

___

Abilities that the job uses

___

___

This job is the best one I could possibly have because

___

Name Date Period

Chapter 10
Workbook Activity
57

Informational Interviews

A. Directions Use this form to help you prepare for an informational interview. Check off each step as you complete it.

Checklist for Calling to Request an Informational Interview

_____ **1)** Say your name and that you are a student at ______________ High School.

_____ **2)** Say that you are interested in learning more about ______________ (career).

_____ **3)** Explain how you know the person works in that career.

_____ **4)** Ask if you can talk to him or her about the career.

_____ **5)** If yes, arrange a time, day, and place to meet.

_____ **6)** If no, thank the person and ask if he or she can suggest someone else to interview.

_____ **7)** Get directions if you need them.

_____ **8)** Write down the appointment on your calendar or appointment book.

B. Directions Here are some questions to ask during an informational interview. Add two questions of your own to the list.

Informational Interview Questions

1) What is your job title?

2) What are the main things you do in your job?

3) What kind of education or training did you get for this job?

4) What skills and abilities make a person good at this job?

5) Do you enjoy your job?

6) What do you like best about the job?

7) What things about the job are difficult or challenging?

8) Can you give me an idea of the salary range for a job like this?

9) What kinds of opportunities are there in your field right now?

10) What kinds of opportunities do you expect in the future?

11) ____

12) ____

Name Date Period

Chapter 10
Workbook Activity
58

Learn While You Earn

Finding a part-time job while you are still a student can be a real challenge. Some students solve this problem by starting small businesses of their own. In this way, the students get firsthand job experience and some training while they earn money. Here is a list of possible business ideas.

- teach computer lessons
- design computer software
- provide a garage sale service
- wash or walk dogs
- grow and sell vegetables
- paint houses
- videotape weddings
- photograph valuables for insurance purposes
- make and sell toys
- wash windows
- design T-shirts
- provide a cleaning service
- repair bicycles
- cater parties
- refinish wood floors
- tutor younger students

Directions Imagine that you are starting a business of your own. Choose one of the ideas listed above, then answer the questions. You may need to do a little research to find the answers.

1) Which business idea did you choose?

____

2) Pick a descriptive name for your business.

____

3) List the equipment and supplies you will need for the business.

____

____

4) How much money will you need to get started? Show how you came up with your estimate.

____

____

5) What will you charge for your services or products?

____

____

6) Can you run the business alone or will you need a partner(s)?

____

7) Who would you ask to be your partner(s)? Explain your choice.

____

____

8) Describe a way to advertise your business.

____

____

9) How much money will you need for advertising? Show how you came up with your estimate.

____

____

10) What kinds of skills will you use or learn in this business?

____

____

Name Date Period

Chapter 10
Workbook Activity
59

Create a Resume

Directions There are many different ways to organize a resume. This form represents one possible format. Complete the form to create a rough draft of a resume.

(Your name)

(Address) (Phone number)

(City, State, Zip) (E-mail address)

Objective

Education

(dates attended) (name of high school)

(degree and any special courses taken)

Work Experience

(dates worked there) (most recent job title)

(description of job duties)

(dates worked there) (most recent job title)

(description of job duties)

Skills

(describe your strengths and special abilities)

References Available on request

Name Date Period

Chapter 10

Workbook Activity 60

Job Sources

A. Directions Match each job source on the left with the correct description on the right. Write the correct letter on each blank.

_____ **1)** employment agency
_____ **2)** chamber of commerce
_____ **3)** classified ads
_____ **4)** vocational rehabilitation service
_____ **5)** state job service
_____ **6)** headhunter
_____ **7)** career and vocational counselor
_____ **8)** networking
_____ **9)** telephone book

a) a good source of information on local businesses
b) a company that helps people find jobs
c) helps people with disabilities find jobs
d) telling many people about your job search so they can help you
e) offered through the state employment office
f) hired by a company to find an employee for a position with specific requirements
g) want ads
h) lists addresses and phone numbers of all kinds of employers
i) helps you choose a profession and find a job; may be free or may charge a fee

B. Directions Read the two classified ads. Then answer the questions.

OFFICE MANAGER
Small, friendly medical practice seeks person to manage staff of 8. Some experience in bookkeeping, accounts receivable, accounts payable, and scheduling preferred. Must have working knowledge of computers. Competitive benefits package and salary. Fax resume to 555-2454.

Classified Ad A

HUMAN RESOURCES ASSISTANT
Medium-size manufacturing company in the southwest suburbs needs HR assistant. This person will be responsible for recruiting employees, maintaining records, new employee orientation, performance reviews, job postings, employee relations, etc. Must be bilingual in English and Spanish. An Associate's degree is required. $25K plus excellent benefits package including health and dental plan, life insurance, disability plan, 401K. Fax resume to 555-2187.

Classified Ad B

1) What high school courses might help prepare you for the job in Ad A?

____

2) What school or community activities or part-time jobs might help prepare you for the job in Ad A? How would they help?

____

____

3) What is the salary of the job in Ad B?

____

4) What are two requirements for the job in Ad B?

____

5) Name the work environment in Ad B.

____

6) What information is in Ad B that is not in Ad A?

____

Name Date Period

Chapter 10

Workbook Activity 61

Interview Questions

Directions Here are some questions that you might be asked during a job interview. Write a short answer to each question. Then role-play a job interview with a classmate, using the interview questions.

1) Why have you chosen to apply for this job?

____

2) How would you describe your personality?

____

3) What are your main strengths?

____

4) What is one of your weaknesses?

____

5) What skills do you have that will help you succeed at a job?

____

6) What work or school experience do you have that will help you succeed at a job?

____

7) In your personal or working life, what is your greatest success?

____

8) In your personal or working life, what is your biggest failure? ______________________________
What did you learn from it?

____

9) Why did you leave your last job?

____

10) Have you ever worked with a group or team to accomplish a goal? Give an example.

____

10) Name three people you admire and tell why you admire them.

____

____

12) Describe your ideal work environment.

____

13) Which school subjects did you like the best and why?

____

____

14) Do you plan to continue your education? If so, what courses will you take?

____

15) What are your long-term goals?

____

Name Date Period

Chapter 10

Workbook Activity 62

Evaluating Benefits

Directions Use this page to think about the importance of the components of a benefits package. Use a 0 to 5 rating scale where 0 = not important at all and 5 = extremely important. Rate each benefit from the point of view of the person described at the top of the column.

Benefit	How Important Is This Benefit to:			
	A person just graduating from high school	A person just graduating from college	Someone 30 years old with two children	You right now
1) health/medical insurance				
2) dental insurance				
3) disability insurance				
4) life insurance				
5) overtime pay				
6) pension program				
7) cafeteria/meal plan				
8) child care				
9) savings plan				
10) stock or investment opportunities				
11) bonus plans				
12) paid vacations				
13) paid holidays				
14) tuition reimbursement				
15) relocation expenses				
16) free parking				
17) employee discounts				
18) flexible work hours				

Name _______________ Date _______ Period _______

Chapter 10
Workbook Activity
63
Page 1

Commuting to and from Work

A. Directions Choose a business in a nearby city that you could get to using a bus, a subway, or a train. Imagine you are commuting to a job in this company. Then gather research on your transportation and fill in the blanks below.

Name of company ______________________________

Street address ______________________________

Circle type of transportation: bus subway train

If you need to be at work at 9:00 A.M., which bus, subway, or train would you take? no. ______ time ______

Will you need to transfer? Yes No If yes, where? ______________________________

What time will the bus or train arrive? ______ How long will it take to get to work? ______________

What time will you need to get up in the morning? ______

If you leave work at 5:00 P.M., which bus, subway, or train will you take home? no. ______ time ______

Will you need to transfer? Yes No If yes, where? ______________________________

What time will the bus or train arrive? _______ What time will you get home? ______

How much will your commute cost per day? ________ per month? ________

B. Directions Now imagine you are commuting to the same job using a car. Fill in the blanks below.

Describe the route you will drive to get to the job.

____

____

____

How long will it take to drive to work during morning rush hour? _________

If you need to start work at 9:00 A.M., what time will you have to leave home? ________

What time will you have to get up in the morning? ________

If you leave work at 5:00 P.M., what time will you get home? ________

Where will you park your car? ______________________________

How much will parking cost per day? ______ per month? ______

Commuting to and from Work, continued

Estimate the cost of gasoline for one week ________ for one month ________

What other factors should you consider when estimating the cost of driving to a job?

____

____

C. Directions Which method of transportation would you use? Explain the reasons for your choice.

Method ____

Reasons ____

____

Name Date Period

Chapter 11

Workbook Activity 64

Beginning a New Job

A. Directions Choose the word from the Word Bank that correctly completes each sentence.

Word Bank

dues	jobs	tax	suitable
handshake	rules	trained	value

1) Reporting early for your first day at work shows that you ______________ your job.

2) Make sure that your outfit is ______________ for work.

3) Your employer might ask you to fill out ______________ forms for the government.

4) Be sure to review the company ______________ in your employee handbook.

5) During a probation period, a worker is ______________ for a job and gets paid for the work.

6) Many workers join a labor union made up of people with similar ______________.

7) Members of a labor union pay ______________ to the organization.

8) A firm ______________ shows coworkers that you want to develop good relationships with them.

B. Directions Answer the questions using complete sentences.

1) Give three examples of information contained in most employee handbooks.

____

____

____

2) Give three examples of information you might find out from a coworker on your first day of work.

____

____

____

Name Date Period

Chapter 11
Workbook Activity 65

Managing Your Time

A. Directions Complete the chart to see how you used your time yesterday. On the left side of the chart, write down the amount of time you spent doing activities you had to do. On the right side, write down the amount of time you spent doing things you enjoy.

Required Activity	Total Time		Leisure Activity	Total Time
Sleeping			Watching TV	
Eating			Talking on phone	
Work			Exercising	
School			Hobbies	
Other:			Other:	

B. Directions Answer the questions.

1) What was the total amount of time you spent on required activities?

____

2) What was the total amount of time you spent on leisure activities?

____

3) What changes could you make to use your time more efficiently?

____

____

Name _______________ Date _______ Period _______

Chapter 11

Workbook Activity 66

Developing Good Communication Skills

A. Directions Put a + sign next to the statements that describe good listening skills. Put a – sign next to the statements that describe poor listening skills.

_____ **1)** Interrupt the speaker.

_____ **2)** Make eye contact with the speaker.

_____ **3)** Ask questions about what the speaker has said.

_____ **4)** Walk away before the speaker has finished talking.

_____ **5)** Turn to another person as the speaker is talking.

_____ **6)** Repeat the speaker's message in your own words.

_____ **7)** Encourage the speaker to tell more about a topic.

B. Directions Review the list above. How often do you act in each of the manners described? Write 1 on the lines below if you often act that way. Write 3 if you sometimes act that way. Write 5 if you seldom act that way.

_____ **1)** Interrupt the speaker.

_____ **2)** Make eye contact with the speaker.

_____ **3)** Ask questions about what the speaker has said.

_____ **4)** Walk away before the speaker has finished talking.

_____ **5)** Turn to another person as the speaker is talking.

_____ **6)** Repeat the speaker's message in your own words.

_____ **7)** Encourage the speaker to tell more about a topic.

C. Directions Answer the question.

How would you describe your listening skills?

____

Name Date Period

Chapter 11
Workbook Activity
67

Body Language

A. Directions Match each statement on the left with the appropriate body language described on the right. Write the correct letter on each blank.

____ **1)** "That was the funniest thing I've ever heard you say!"

____ **2)** "I'm really glad to be working with you today."

____ **3)** "I shouldn't have stayed up watching that movie last night."

____ **4)** "I can't wait till lunch time. I'm absolutely starving!"

____ **5)** "Tell me what I can do to help you."

____ **6)** "I disagree. I think we should do it this way."

____ **7)** "I don't know how it happened. I was so careful."

a) tap fingers on desktop

b) arms extended outward

c) chuckle

d) yawn

e) smile

f) arms crossed

g) wringing hands

B. Directions Answer the questions.

1) What message do you receive from a listener who frowns and taps her foot while you are talking?

____

2) What message do you receive from a listener who nods his or her head as you speak?

____

3) What message do you receive from a speaker who will not make eye contact with you while speaking?

____

Name Date Period

Chapter 11
Workbook Activity 68

Belonging to a Team

A. Directions Answer the questions using complete sentences.

1) What teams have you belonged to?

____

____

2) What was your role on the team?

____

____

3) What tasks were completed by other members of the team?

____

____

4) How did the team decide which tasks each member would complete?

____

____

5) Did a member of your team ever fail to complete his or her job? What happened?

____

____

B. Directions Put an X by the words that describe a good team member.

____ **1)** selfish

____ **2)** knowledgeable

____ **3)** dedicated

____ **4)** bored

____ **5)** energetic

____ **6)** stingy

____ **7)** clever

____ **8)** friendly

____ **9)** helpful

____ **10)** quarrelsome

Name Date Period

Chapter 11
Workbook Activity 69

Dealing with Workplace Issues

A. Directions Choose the word from the Word Bank that correctly completes each sentence.

Word Bank

bothering	comfortable	gender	right
businesslike	ethnic	policy	workplace

1) Some people are discriminated against because of their ______________.

2) The law forbids discrimination in the ______________.

3) Harassment is repeatedly ______________ a person at work.

4) Because of harassment, a worker does not feel ______________ in the workplace.

5) Constantly telling ______________ jokes can be called harassment.

6) Every company should have a ______________ on discrimination and harassment.

7) You should always speak to coworkers in a ______________ manner.

8) Every worker has a ______________ to be treated fairly at work.

B. Directions Answer the questions using complete sentences.

1) Your supervisor keeps asking you to go out to dinner. You are beginning to feel uncomfortable around your supervisor. What should you do?

____

____

2) You have put some pictures of your favorite TV star in your locker. A coworker tells you that the pictures make him or her feel uncomfortable and asks you to remove them. What will you do?

____

____

Name Date Period

Chapter 11
Workbook Activity
70

Choosing a Career

A. Directions The people described here have their own special qualities and skills. Name two careers you think may be suited to each person.

1) Rick loves being outdoors. His best subject in school is science. Rick's friends tell him he has a "green thumb."

Possible careers : ____________________ ____________________

2) Marta is the oldest of five children. She can't remember a time when she did not have to watch a younger brother or sister. Marta doesn't mind, though. She enjoys playing games with children.

Possible careers : ____________________ ____________________

3) Sue's best subject in school is math. She is always helping family members balance their checkbooks. A few months ago, Sue helped a friend make a personal budget. Now the friend has saved enough money for a down payment on a car.

Possible careers : ____________________ ____________________

4) Bill enjoys working out. He exercises daily at the local gym. Bill has helped other members of the gym make personal exercise plans.

Possible careers : ____________________ ____________________

5) Wanda enjoys driving and has a great sense of direction. She has driven just about every type of car ever invented. When faced with a traffic jam, Wanda can always think of an alternative route to get to her destination.

Possible careers : ____________________ ____________________

B. Directions Select one individual described above. Imagine the person asked you how he or she could learn more about the careers you identified. Describe your response on the lines below.

____

____

____

____

Name Date Period

Chapter 11
Workbook Activity 71

Performance Assessments

A. Directions Put a check on the blank in front of each item you would expect to find on a performance assessment.

____ **1)** Worker's name

____ **2)** Supervisor's name

____ **3)** Date the worker began working for the company

____ **4)** Age of the worker

____ **5)** Names of coworkers

____ **6)** List of work tasks

____ **7)** Date the supervisor and worker met to review the assessment

____ **8)** Worker's hourly pay rate

____ **9)** Supervisor's signature

____ **10)** Supervisor's salary

B. Directions Suppose you think your supervisor has not been fair when completing your performance assessment. Describe what you could do.

____

____

____

____

____

Name ______ Date ______ Period ______

Chapter 11

Workbook Activity 72

Learning New Skills

A. Directions Choose the word from the Word Bank that correctly completes each sentence.

Word Bank

change	hobby	life	valuable
courses	library	online	workplace

1) Since your job can ______________ over time, it is important to learn new skills.

2) Some companies offer ______________ for workers.

3) Community schools often offer courses to develop a ______________ such as sewing or golf.

4) Some courses help you master ______________ skills such as reading and making a budget.

5) A local ______________ may have information about courses in the community.

6) Many colleges offer ______________ instruction.

7) On-the-job training allows workers to develop new skills in the ______________.

8) Learning new skills makes you a ______________ worker.

B. Directions Answer the questions using complete sentences.

1) What hobby would you like to develop? How would you go about developing it?

____

____

____

2) What life skill would you like to develop? How would you go about developing it?

____

____

____

Name Date Period

Chapter 11

Workbook Activity 73

Asking for a Raise

A. Directions You think you deserve a raise in your allowance. Write two reasons why you feel you should have this raise. Give concrete examples to support your reasons. Then decide when to approach your parents or guardians to ask for the raise. Set a time with them and refer to your reasons and examples when you meet.

Reasons you deserve a raise	Examples
1) ______________________	1) ______________________
______________________	______________________
2) ______________________	2) ______________________
______________________	______________________

B. Directions Answer the questions about the results of your meeting.

1) Did you obtain the raise you wanted? ______________________

2) Would you do anything differently the next time you ask for a raise? Explain your answer.

____

____

____

3) Do you think asking for a raise in a job situation would be similar? Explain your answer.

____

____

____

Name Date Period

Chapter 11

Workbook Activity 74

Experiencing a Loss

Directions Think about a time when you lost something that you loved. Then answer the questions.

1) What did you lose?

2) Did the loss come as a surprise or did you suspect it might happen?

3) What three words best describe your feelings at the time of the loss.

4) How did the loss affect your daily life activities?

5) Whom did you talk with about your loss?

6) What actions did you take to move through your sadness?

7) How long did it take for you to get over your loss?

8) How is your experience similar to that of a worker suddenly losing a job?

9) What advice would you give to a worker who is trying to deal with the sudden loss of his or her job?

10) What actions could the worker take to deal with the loss?

Name Date Period

Postsecondary School Questions

A. Directions Here are some questions an admissions officer might ask during an interview. Write a short answer to each question.

1) What were your favorite courses in high school?

____

____

2) What extracurricular activities have you participated in?

____

____

3) What are some of your hobbies?

____

____

4) What jobs have you had?

____

____

5) What achievement pleases you the most and why?

____

____

6) What are your career goals?

____

____

7) Why do you want to go to college?

____

____

8) What do you hope to major in? Why have you chosen this major?

____

____

Postsecondary School Questions, continued

9) Why are you interested in this school?

10) Why should this school accept you?

11) What questions do you have about this college?

B. Directions Imagine you are visiting a college campus and have an opportunity to talk to a student who attends the school. Write four questions you might ask the student.

1) ___

2) ___

3) ___

4) ___

Name ______ Date ______ Period ______

Chapter 12

Workbook Activity 76

Application Checklist

A. Directions Here is a checklist you can use when completing college applications. Use the checklist to complete the vocabulary activity below.

- Read the entire application before you begin to fill it out.
- Arrange for each college to receive a transcript of your high school grades.
- Have the College Entrance Examination Board report SAT and achievement test results to the college (and/or make arrangements for ACT scores to be reported).
- Give a counselor recommendation form to your guidance counselor to complete.
- Request recommendations from your teachers.
- Type or print all factual information required on the application.
- Write a rough draft of the essay.
- Ask teachers, parents, and/or friends to read your essay, make suggestions, and proofread it for any errors in grammar, punctuation, and spelling.
- Type or print the final version of the essay on the application form.
- Enclose a check for the application fee.
- Put your return address and correct postage on the envelope.
- Deadline for application form is ______.
- Mail completed application form on ______.
- Deadline for financial aid forms is ______.
- Mail financial aid forms on ______.
- Acceptances will be mailed by ______.
- Offer must be accepted by ______.

B. Directions Find each word listed here in the checklist above and circle it. Then write a short definition for each word.

1) application ______

2) transcript ______

3) SAT ______

4) achievement test ______

5) guidance counselor ______

6) recommendation ______

7) rough draft ______

8) financial aid form ______

Name Date Period

Researching Special Services

Directions Here is a list of questions to ask about the special services a postsecondary school offers. Add two questions of your own to this list. Choose a school you are considering or any local college. Then contact the school to find the answers to these questions.

1) If a student has a learning disability, how will the information about the learning disability be used when the student's application is reviewed?

____

2) What special services do you offer for students with disabilities?

____

____

3) Is there a charge for the services?

____

4) Is there an adviser who works specifically with students with learning disabilities?

____

5) Are students given access to aids such as tape recorders, taped texts, and note-takers? How would a student arrange for these services?

____

____

6) How would a student arrange for modified exams (extra time, oral tests)?

____

7) How would a student arrange for tutoring?

____

8) What kind of training do the tutors have?

____

9) Are there support groups for students with disabilities on the campus?

____

10) What types of accommodations have been made for students with special needs?

____

____

11) ______________________________

12) ______________________________

Name Date Period

Chapter 12

Workbook Activity 78

Identifying Strengths and Weaknesses

A. Directions Before choosing study strategies, it is helpful to identify your own strengths and weaknesses. Consider your experiences in each of these areas when you complete this form. Put a check mark in the My Strengths column for those that are strengths for you.

	My Strengths	My Weaknesses
1) General Study Habits		
2) Memorizing Information		
3) Listening		
4) Taking Notes		
5) Planning and Organizing		
6) Preparing for Tests		
7) Taking Tests		
8) Using Textbooks		
9) Using Other Resources		
10) Oral Communication		

B. Directions Look at the form again. Write on the lines below how you could improve each area that is not a strength. Refer to the textbook for specific strategy steps.

Name Date Period

Chapter 12

Workbook Activity 79

Financial Aid

Directions Match each description with the correct word in the box. Write the correct letter on the blank before each description.

_____ **1)** Financial aid that depends on a student's academic or athletic merit, and does not depend on the existence of financial need

_____ **2)** The amount of money you and your family are expected to be able to pay for your education.

_____ **3)** The amount of money the federal government expects the student to contribute to his or her education. Usually a student is expected to contribute about 1/3 of his or her savings and 1/2 of his or her summer earnings.

_____ **4)** A gift of money to pay for tuition

_____ **5)** A short time period after graduation during which the borrower is not required to begin repayment. The typical time is six or nine months.

_____ **6)** Anything that lowers the cost of college for a student.

_____ **7)** An amount charged to the borrower for the privilege of using the lender's money. It is usually calculated as a percentage of the principal.

_____ **8)** A kind of financial aid that is repaid, with interest.

_____ **9)** A form used to apply for financial aid.

_____ **10)** Financial aid that the government gives based on need.

a) grace period

b) FAFSA

c) loan

d) student contribution

e) scholarship

f) grant

g) financial aid

h) merit-based

i) interest

j) expected family contribution

Name Date Period

Chapter 13
Workbook Activity 80

What Are You Looking for in a Marriage Partner?

A. Directions Write some characteristics you would look for in a spouse under the categories listed here.

1) Family life preferences (examples: wants children, wants pets)

2) Goals and interests (Examples: sports, outdoor activities)

3) Physical appearance and personality (examples: beautiful or ordinary, funny or serious)

B. Directions Answer the questions.

1) How many of the characteristics you listed are similar to your own characteristics? Is that important? Explain your answer.

2) Do you think your family will have an influence on whom you marry? Explain your answer.

Name Date Period

Chapter 13
Workbook Activity 81

Caring for a Baby

Through the following activity, you can learn more about the responsibilities of parenting. You will need a 5-pound sack of flour or sand, a sense of humor, and a little imagination. The sack of flour or sand is the "baby."

A. Directions Individually or with a partner, you will care for the "baby." Every day for one week, you must dress and watch over the baby. To dress the baby, you must make a container that protects it from harm. You must always have the baby nearby or arrange for someone you trust to care for it temporarily if you cannot.

B. Directions At the end of the week, answer these questions.

1) Did you care for the baby alone or did a classmate share the responsibility?

____

2) Describe two insights you gained about parenting through this activity.

____

____

3) What was the most rewarding part of caring for the baby? Explain your answer.

____

____

____

4) What was the most challenging part about caring for the baby? Explain your answer.

____

____

____

____

5) Has this activity changed the way you think about parenting? If so, how?

____

____

____

____

Name Date Period

Chapter 13
Workbook Activity 82

Identify Your Learning Style

Everyone has a preferred learning style. By identifying whether your learning style is visual, auditory, or tactile, you will be able to learn more effectively.

A. Directions Place a check mark next to each statement that describes you.

Column A

____ **1)** I feel comfortable standing while working.

____ **2)** I fidget, or move around, a lot.

____ **3)** I learn through movement and exploring my environment.

____ **4)** I like to chew gum or eat in class.

____ **5)** I like to collect things.

____ **6)** I like to listen to music while I'm working.

____ **7)** I like to take things apart and put them back together.

____ **8)** I often reach out to touch things.

____ **9)** I talk fast and use my hands to communicate.

____ **10)** I am comfortable hugging and touching other people to show friendship.

____ **11)** I am good at sports.

____ **12)** People have called me hyperactive.

Column B

____ **13)** I can understand and follow directions on maps.

____ **14)** I have a hard time getting the words to a song right.

____ **15)** I like charts, diagrams, and maps.

____ **16)** I like the volume on the radio and TV really high.

____ **17)** I like to take notes to review later.

____ **18)** I often need to have verbal instructions repeated.

____ **19)** I remember information best by writing it several times or drawing pictures and diagrams.

____ **20)** I remember things best by picturing them in my head.

____ **221)** I watch speakers' facial expressions and body language.

____ **22)** I am a good speller.

____ **23)** I am good at drawing, painting, and other visual arts.

____ **24)** I am good at solving jigsaw puzzles.

Column C

____ **25)** I don't like to read text on a computer screen, especially when there is a fancy background design.

____ **26)** I follow verbal directions better than written ones.

____ **27)** I like to tell jokes and stories.

____ **28)** I need diagrams, graphs, and maps explained to me.

____ **29)** I often sing, hum, or whistle to myself.

____ **30)** I often remember things by making up a musical jingle.

____ **31)** I talk to myself.

____ **32)** I understand better when I read aloud.

____ **33)** I use my finger as a pointer when reading.

____ **34)** I would rather listen to a lecture than read a textbook.

____ **35)** I would rather listen to music than look at a painting.

____ **36)** My notebooks are pretty messy.

B. Directions Count the number of check marks in each column. If Column A has the greatest number of check marks, you are probably a tactile learner. If Column B has the greatest number of check marks, you are probably a visual learner. If Column C has the greatest number of check marks, you are probably an auditory learner. Write your learning style on the line below.

____

Personal Journal, Chapter 1, p. 22

Personal Journal, Chapter 1, p. 23

Personal Journal, Chapter 2, p. 65

Personal Journal, Chapter 2, p. 82

Personal Journal, Chapter 3, p. 102

Personal Journal, Chapter 3, p. 109

Personal Journal, Chapter 4, p. 118

Personal Journal, Chapter 4, p. 134

Personal Journal, Chapter 5, p. 153

Personal Journal, Chapter 5, p. 163

Personal Journal, Chapter 6, p. 173

Personal Journal, Chapter 6, p. 197

Personal Journal, Chapter 7, p. 229

Personal Journal, Chapter 7, p. 235

Personal Journal, Chapter 8, p. 243

Personal Journal, Chapter 8, p. 258

Personal Journal, Chapter 9, p. 279

Personal Journal, Chapter 9, p. 287

Personal Journal, Chapter 10, p. 303

Personal Journal, Chapter 10, p. 319

Personal Journal, Chapter 11, p. 356

Personal Journal, Chapter 11, p. 357

Personal Journal, Chapter 12, p. 391

Personal Journal, Chapter 12, p. 398

Personal Journal, Chapter 13, p. 414

Personal Journal, Chapter 13, p. 418